READ WITH Biff, Chip & Kipper

Let's Get Ready for School

Activity Book

OXFORD
UNIVERSITY PRESS

OXFORD
UNIVERSITY PRESS

Great Clarendon Street, Oxford, OX2 6DP, United Kingdom

Oxford University Press is a department of the University of Oxford. It furthers the University's objective of excellence in research, scholarship, and education by publishing worldwide. Oxford is a registered trade mark of Oxford University Press in the UK and in certain other countries

Text © Oxford University Press 2017
Floppy and the Bone text © Cynthia Rider 2005
Missing! text © Roderick Hunt 2006
Illustrations © Alex Brychta

The characters in this work are the original creation of Roderick Hunt and Alex Brychta who retain copyright in the characters.

The moral rights of the author have been asserted

First published 2017

Series editor: Annemarie Young
Activities created by Isabel Thomas

British Library Cataloguing in Publication Data
Data available

ISBN: 978-0-19-275924-5

10 9 8 7 6 5 4 3 2 1

Paper used in the production of this book is a natural, recyclable product made from wood grown in sustainable forests. The manufacturing process conforms to the environmental regulations of the country of origin.

Printed in China

Introduction

Sharing stories is one of the best ways to prepare children for starting school. In this book, favourite stories form a springboard for fun activities that will get your child ready for reading, writing and maths.

- Stories with familiar settings build vocabulary and knowledge about the world. Children will enjoy retelling the stories using pictures or props.

- Talking about characters and their feelings helps children to develop social skills, and feel more confident in new situations.

- Story-based play also helps children to develop their own creativity and thinking, and is an opportunity to use the new words they have learned.

This book includes two lively *Read with Biff, Chip & Kipper* stories to share with your child. Each story is followed by activities that develop first skills. There are ideas for talking about the stories, as well as hands-on activities and games.

At the centre of the book you'll find letter-sound and number cards to pull out and use in activities and games. Along with the ideas in this book, they will help you to share other stories in the same way.

The best way to encourage your child is to offer lots of praise. When they complete a set of activities, the sticker symbol in the corner of the page indicates which sticker they can stick onto the poster as a reward.

Letter-sound and number cards

Stickers

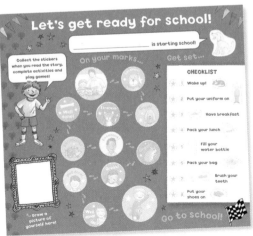

Poster

Floppy and the Bone

Floppy saw a big bone.

Floppy got the bone!

But Floppy did not drop the bone!

He ran up the hill.

He ran into a wood...

and onto a bridge...
and he stopped!

Floppy looked down. He saw
a dog in the water.

The dog had a big bone.

Floppy wanted that
bone, too.

Grrrrrrrrrr! went Floppy.

SPLASH! went the bone.
SPLASH! went Floppy.

"Oh no!" said Floppy.
"The dog I saw was me!"

Sharing stories

Ask questions about the story.

What did Floppy see in the water? Was it a real dog?

Why did Floppy drop his bone?

 Draw lines to show how Floppy feels in each picture.

excited

cross

scared

 Sit in front of a mirror. Make faces to show how the characters feel.

Put the sticker on the poster

Making marks

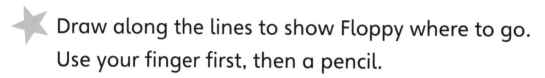

Retell the story of Floppy and the Bone, using the pictures to help.

⭐ Draw along the lines to show Floppy where to go.
Use your finger first, then a pencil.

 **along the street**

●- -

 **through the woods**

●- -

 over the bridge

●- -

Help Floppy get to the bone. Find a letter-sound card that matches the first letter of each thing he goes past.

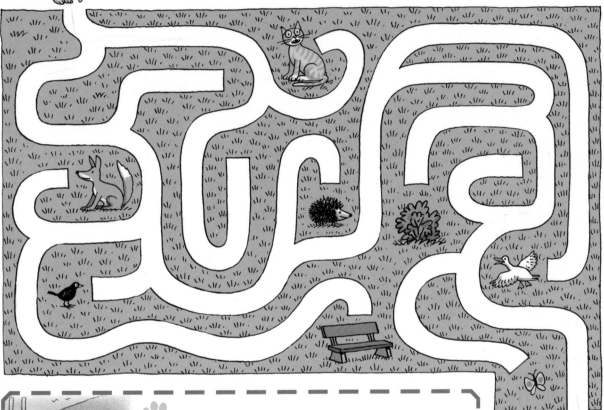

🐾 **Draw a map together to show the places Floppy ran in the story.**

🐾 **Can your child think of a name for each place?**

🐾 **Write down your child's ideas as labels on the map.**

9

Put the sticker on the poster

Comparing things

Look at the detail in the story pictures.

How many different animals can you spot?

 Colour the longest bone blue.
Colour the shortest bone red.

 Draw a circle around the biggest dog.
Draw a triangle around the smallest dog.

Who is the tallest?

Who is the shortest?

Which bowl holds the most water?

Build a bridge out of books. Put a mirror under the bridge.

Use a toy dog to act out the story.

Can your child put the dog **on** the bridge, **under** the bridge, or **in** the water?

Put the sticker on the poster

Spotting patterns

How many butterflies can you spot in the story?

⭐ Draw a line to join butterflies that look the same.

12

Which butterfly comes next? Colour it in.

Count the butterflies of the same colour in each line. Find the right number cards and write the number in the box.

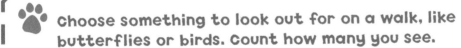
Choose something to look out for on a walk, like butterflies or birds. Count how many you see.

Make a simple pattern using small objects or stickers. Ask your child to add the next object to continue the pattern.

Ask your child to count each type of object in the pattern. Then count how many objects there are altogether and label them with a number card.

Put the sticker on the poster

Listening for sounds

Play **I Spy** using the story pictures. For example, how many things can you find beginning with the sound 'b' as in 'bike'?

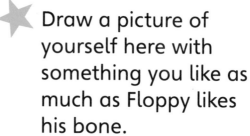

⭐ Look in a mirror. Watch what your mouth and tongue do as they make the sounds: 'a', 'th', 'r', 'm', 'o'.

⭐ Draw a picture of yourself here with something you like as much as Floppy likes his bone.

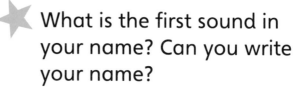

⭐ What is the first sound in your name? Can you write your name?

....

 Choose a sound. Go on a treasure hunt for things that start with that sound.

put the sticker on the poster

14

Missing!

Nadim had a hamster.
He called it Jaws.

"Jaws is a funny name
for a hamster," said Biff.

Nadim put Jaws in his cage, but
he forgot to shut the cage door.

Jaws got out of the cage and ran off.

Nadim saw the cage was open. "Oh no!" he said.

Nadim was upset. "Jaws has run off," said Nadim.

"We can look for him," said Biff. They looked and looked.

Biff looked under the sink. Chip looked in the fridge.
Nadim looked under the cupboard.

Nadim's dad looked under the floor.
"Is Jaws down here?" he said.

Let's get Floppy. He can help us.

Look in there.

Then Chip had an idea.

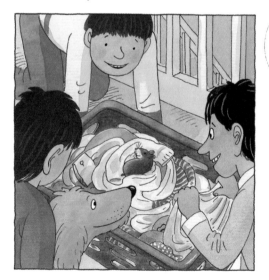

Look! You can see why I called him Jaws.

Jaws was in the clothes basket. He had made a nest.

22

Telling stories

Why was Nadim upset when Jaws ran away?

Have you ever lost something?

 What do you think Jaws did next?
Draw a picture of his adventures.

 Make a home or nest for a toy animal. Will you choose materials that are smooth or rough, soft or hard?

 Talk about how you will care for your toy pet.

 Draw or write a list of foods that your toy pet eats.

Put the sticker on the poster

23

Counting

Count things that you see in the story.

How many holes did Jaws chew in the T-shirt?

⭐ Count these things from the story. How many are there in each row?

⭐ Can you find a number card that matches each row?

Help Jaws get back to his cage. Pick a number card and count the dots on it. Colour the same number of footprints. Keep playing until you reach the cage.

 Choose two places. Count how many steps it takes you to get between them.

 Ask your child to share out a bunch of grapes. How many grapes does each person get?

 Leave a small pile of similar objects for your child to sort into groups. How many in each group? How many altogether?

Put the sticker on the poster

Matching and sorting

Why do you think Jaws hid in the clothes basket?

⭐ Dad is pegging out the washing.
Count the socks on each line.

⭐ Draw one more sock on each line and colour
them in. How many socks are there now?

Decorate this sock with triangles.

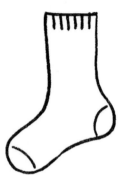

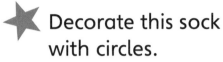 Decorate this sock with circles.

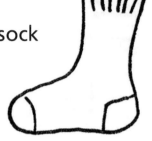

 Decorate this sock with squares.

 Decorate this sock with rectangles.

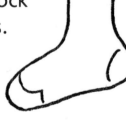

 Collect small objects (socks, buttons or blocks). Sort them by colour, shape or pattern.

 Count the objects in each group and put the right number card next to each group.

 Which pile has more? Which pile has less?

Put the sticker on the poster

Playing number games

Jaws loves nuts. How many nuts can you find hidden in the story?

⭐ Count the nuts in each row.
Find the right number card for each row.

⭐ Which row has the most nuts? Which has the least nuts?

Draw the right number of nuts in each bowl.

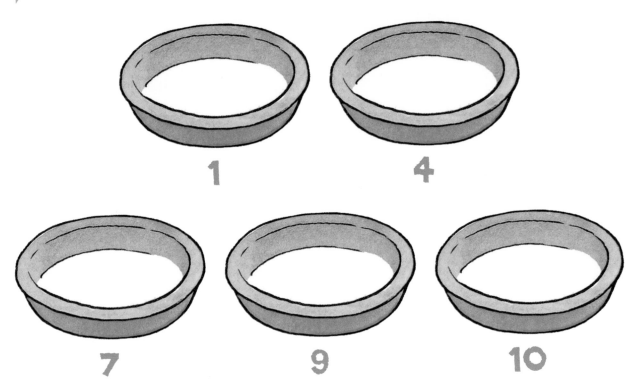

1

4

7

9

10

 Roll a dice or pick a number card. How many different ways can your child show that number? For example, collecting objects, star jumps, making marks on paper.

 Spot digits around the house, for example, when cooking or baking together, on controls, clocks and keypads.

Put the sticker on the poster

Playing sound games

Say the names of the characters in the story. What is the first sound in each name?

⭐ Help the children find Jaws. Take turns to roll a dice. Move a counter along the path. Say the name of the object you land on. What is the first sound in that word?

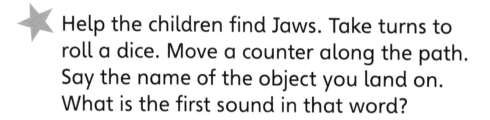

f Start

t

n

s

c

e

Find me!

v End

k

y

a

q

30

⭐ Can you find the matching letter-sound card for each square you land on?

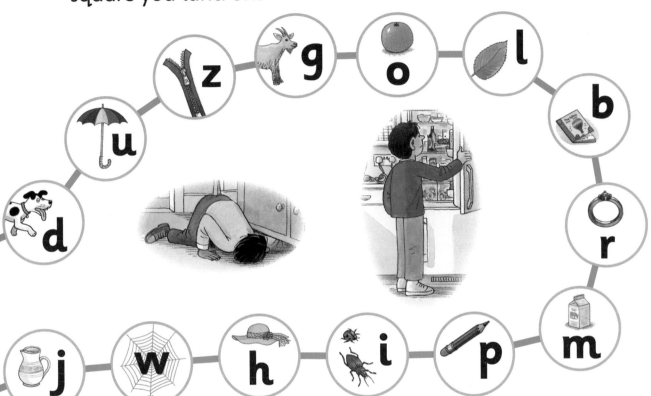

🐾 Play the game again. This time you have to name an animal or type of food that begins with each letter sound you land on.

🐾 Pick a card. Say the sound. Find an object that begins with that sound.

Put the sticker on the poster

More activities

Use your letter-sound cards and number cards to play these games. They will help your child to learn that letters represent sounds, and digits represent numbers.

Recognizing numbers

- Hide the number cards around the house. Ask your child to call the numbers out as they find them.
- Jumble up the number cards. Ask your child to put them in the right order. Start with 1 to 5. Move on to 1 to 10 when your child is ready.
- Pick a number card at random. Build a tower using that number of blocks.
- Slide a paperclip on to each number card. Use a magnet on a string to fish for the numbers in order.
- Share out small objects. Count the number in each group. Use the number cards as labels.
- Put the number cards in the right order. Pick a number. Ask which numbers come before and after that number.
- Use a paperclip to join a number card to ten different socks. Can you peg them on the line in the right order?

Recognizing letter sounds

- Look at the pictures on the back of the letter-sound cards. Say the first sound in each word.
- Lay out four objects and four letter-sound cards that match the first sound of each word, for example, a sock, an apple, a toothbrush and a pencil and the letter-sound cards s, a, t and p. Ask your child to help you match the letters/sounds to the objects.
- Point to a letter in a book or comic. Ask your child to find the matching letter-sound card.
- Trace around the letter shapes with your finger.
- Choose one letter shape. Look for opportunities to form it in different ways, e.g. draw it in chalk, make it out of sticks or stones, paint it, make it out of food, write it in bubbles in the bath, write it in the air.

When you share these games with your child, make sure you play too! Pretend to get some answers wrong so that your child can correct you.